# SLEEPING
## LIKE THE
# PROPHET ﷺ

WRITTEN BY MOIN UDDIN KHAN
ILLUSTRATED BY KAMRUL HUSSAIN

# SLEEPING
## LIKE THE
# PROPHET

Published by IDEA Press
Copyright © IDEA Press 2019
2nd Edition
ISBN 978-0-9929736-1-2
A Project of SHADE

**Proceeds generated from the sales of these publications will go towards SHADE which is a UK registered charity.**

To purchase 'Just Like The Prophet' series and other publications please contact:

w: alrawda.org
e: info@alrawda.org
t: +44 (0) 20 7998 7768

# Author's Note

All praise to Allah Lord of the worlds and salutations upon His
Messenger Muhammad ﷺ.

This book teaches the Sunnah practices of the Prophet Muhammad ﷺ
in terms of sleeping. It mentions over 40 etiquette in sequence and in
simple rhyming English.

This endeavour was to provide an alternative to the common nursery
rhymes and to help develop an Islamic identity. Every line has at least
one Sunnah backed by a verse of the Holy Qur'an or Hadith. Even
though it's aimed towards children, adults can also benefit by the
rhyming easy to remember lines.

An immense amount of effort has been made to bring this project to
this stage. We would like to thank all those who have supported us with
their time, effort and funds.

Whatever is correct of this work is from Allah and His Messenger.ﷺ
Whatever mistakes therein is from myself and Shaytan.

Moin Uddin Khan
*(a humble servant in need of Allah)*
London, UK
Muharram 1436 / November 2014

*Dedicated to my beautiful children*
*who have been my source of inspiration*
*and motivation in this work.*

Allah almighty made humans in perfect form,
He made Muhammad ﷺ the best to be born,
from his life there are inspirations to be drawn,
we should follow him in the way he has shown.

1

He would mention Allah's name,
as he entered his home.

He would greet with *salam*, even if he was alone.

He would brush his teeth with a *miswak* and would comb his hair.

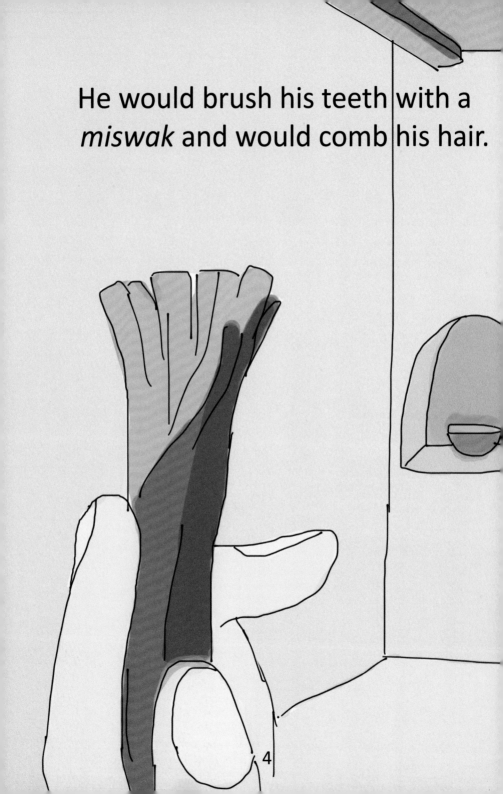

4

He would perform *wudhu,*
just like he did for prayer.

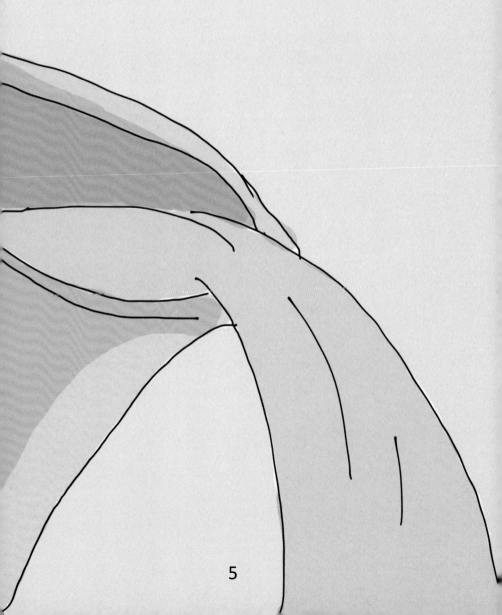

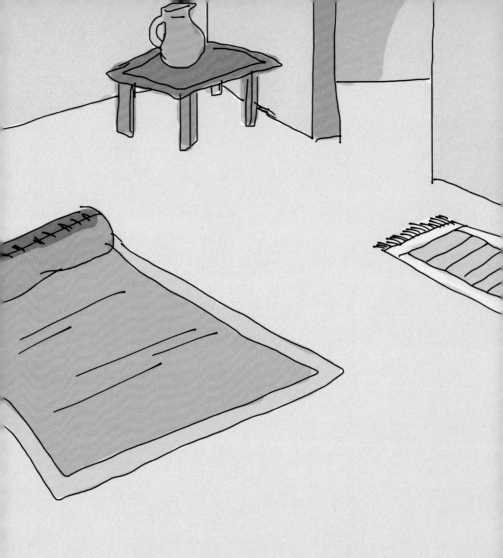

His bedding was on a mat,
placed on the floor.

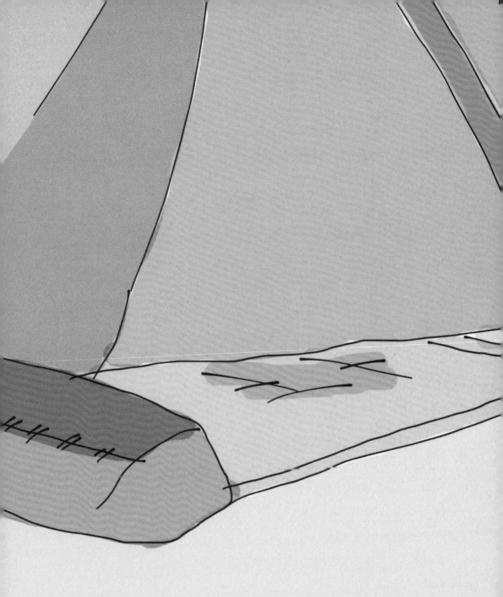

His pillow was of leather,
filled with leaves and straw.

He would take a nap at midday,
whilst the sun was at its peak.

8

Before getting into bed,
thrice he would dust the sheet.

Reading two *Quls* on his palms,
he would wipe from head to feet.

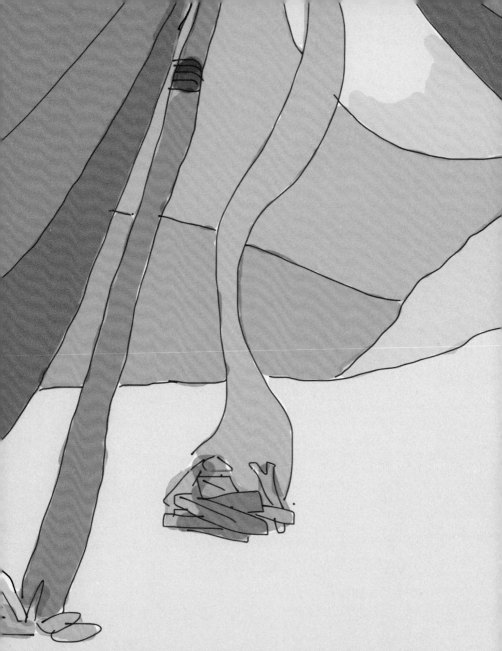

He would not lie on his stomach,
as Allah would be displeased.

He would lie on his right side,
placing his palm under his cheek.

Had anybody wronged him,
he would make sure to forgive.

He would lie facing the *Qibla*, and lastly he would read,

*"With your name oh Allah,
I shall die and I shall live"*

His eyes would be shut,
but his heart would not sleep.

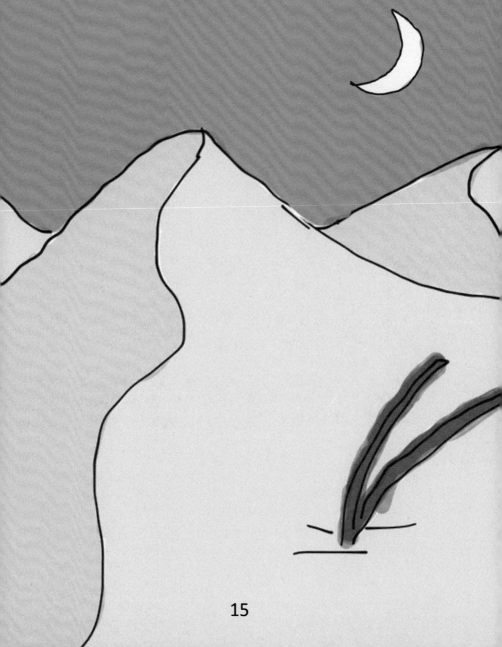

If he had a good dream,
its virtue he would preach.

For those who had a bad dream,
about it they should not speak.

Spitting to the left thrice,
Allah's refuge they should seek.

He would awaken after a few hours,
in the darkness of the night.

His sides forsaking the bed,
quietly he would rise.

20

Pondering over the creation, he would wipe the sleep from his eyes.

*"Praise to Allah who gave us life
after death, and with him
we shall revive"*

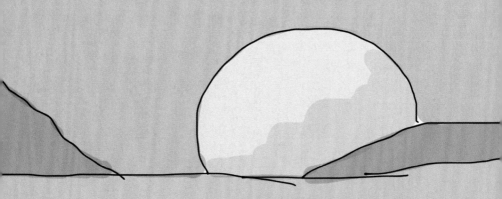

With hope and fear in front of his Lord, the *Qur'an* he would recite.

When passing verses of mercy,
he would seek it with desire.

When passing verses of punishment,
he could not restrain the cries.

His feet would swell due to standing,
his devotion would not tire.

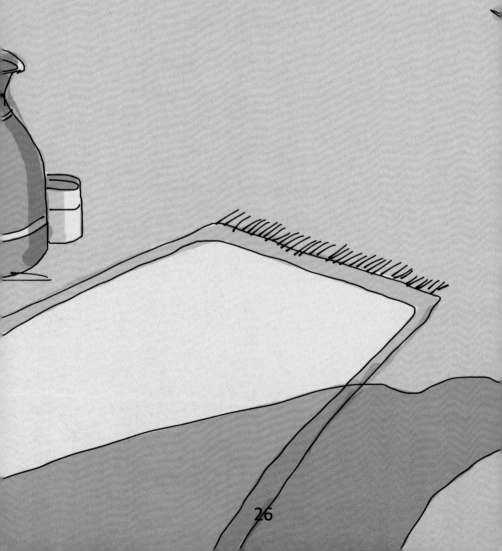

Despite Allah had forgiven his
future mistakes, as well as his prior.

To be a grateful servant,
he would yearn to acquire.

A portion of the night he spent in prayer, thereafter he would retire.

At the break of dawn he would rise, upon hearing the call of the *adhan.*

Offering his prayers to his Lord,
is how his day began.

We pray that we act accordingly,
in the best way that we can.
Amin.

## Easy Memorisation

He would mention Allah's name, as he entered his home.
He would greet with salam, even if he was alone.
He would brush his teeth with a miswak and would comb his hair.
He would perform wudhu, just like he did for prayer.
His bedding was on a mat, placed on the floor.
His pillow was of leather, filled with leaves and straw.
He would take a nap at midday, whilst the sun was at its peak.
Before getting into bed, thrice he would dust the sheets.
Reading two Quls on his palms, he would wipe from head to feet.
He would not lie on his stomach, as Allah would be displeased.
He would lie on his right side, placing his palm under his cheek.
Had anybody wronged him, he would make sure to forgive.
He would lie facing the Qibla, and lastly he would read,
*"With your name oh Allah, I shall die and I shall live"*
His eyes would be shut, but his heart would not sleep.
If he had a good dream, its virtue he would preach.
For those who had a bad dream, about it they should not speak.
Spitting to the left thrice, Allah's refuge they should seek.
He would awaken after a few hours, in the darkness of the night.
His sides forsaking the bed, quietly he would rise.
Pondering over the creation, he would wipe the sleep from his eyes.
*"Praise to Allah who gave us life after death,*
*and with him we shall revive"*
With hope and fear in front of his Lord, the Qur'an he would recite.
When passing verses of mercy, he would seek it with desire.
When passing verses of punishment, he could not restrain the cries.
His feet would swell due to standing, his devotion would not tire.
Despite Allah had forgiven his future mistakes, as well as his prior.
To be a grateful servant, he would yearn to acquire.
A portion of the night he spent in prayer, thereafter he would retire.
At the break of dawn he would rise, upon hearing the call of adhan.
Offering his prayers to his Lord, is how his day began.

'This book is the second publication of the
'Just Like The Prophet Series'

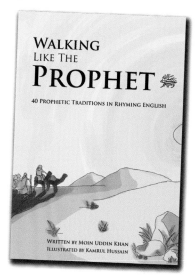

Other books by the author
Life of Muhammad The Sublime: Biography Simply Told in Poetic Rhyme

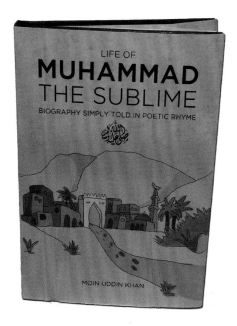

# About SHADE

SHADE is a UK based charitable umbrella organisation, which endeavours to help society tackle many of the challenges it faces. SHADE runs various projects and activities for the community at large, its programmes engage people from all walks of life and brings them together to encourage respect, understanding and tolerance. It has five different sectors in which there are projects dealing with different aspects of an individual's needs. This has been divided into five sectors: Social, Health, Aid, Development & Education.

# Support Us

## Text: IDEA33 £10 to 70070

## Visit: www.theshade.org/donate

## Phone: 020 7998 7768

## Bank Transfer:
## HSBC Bank
## a/c: 12030748
## s/c: 40-02-34

**UK Charity No. 1149699**

The Shade Centre
Unit 1, Church Rd Studios
62 Church Road, London E12 6AF
W: www.theshade.org  |  E: info@theshade.org